How to use this book

Follow the advice, in italics, given for you on each page.
Support the children as they read the text that is shaded in cream.
Praise *the children at every step!*

Detailed guidance is provided in the Read Write Inc. Phonics Handbook

8 reading activities

Children:
- *Practise reading the speed sounds.*
- *Read the green and red words for the story.*
- *Listen as you read the introduction.*
- *Discuss the vocabulary check with you.*
- *Read the story.*
- *Re-read the story and discuss the 'questions to talk about'.*
- *Re-read the story with fluency and expression.*
- *Practise reading the speed words.*

Speed sounds

Consonants *Say the pure sounds (do not add 'uh').*

f (ff)	l (ll)	m mm	n (nn) kn	r rr	s ss	v ve	z zz s	(sh)	th	ng nk

b bb	c k (ck)	d dd	g gg	h	j	p pp	qu	t tt	w wh	x	y	(ch) tch

Vowels *Say the sounds in and out of order.*

at	hen head	in	on	up	day	see happy	high	blow

zoo	look	car	for	fair	whirl	shout	boy

*Each box contains one sound but sometimes more than one grapheme. Focus graphemes are **circled**.*

Green words

Read in Fred Talk (pure sounds).

milk   blob   stu<u>ff</u>   soft   flag   Mr Pun<u>ch</u>

fro<u>ck</u>   pi<u>nk</u>

Read in syllables.

com`ic → comic      bu<u>ck</u>`et → bu<u>ck</u>et

fi<u>sh</u>`y → fi<u>sh</u>y   fu<u>nn</u>`y → fu<u>nn</u>y   yu<u>mm</u>`y → yu<u>mm</u>y   lo<u>ll</u>`y → lo<u>ll</u>y

Read the root word first and then with the ending.

<u>sh</u>e<u>ll</u> → <u>sh</u>e<u>ll</u>s   sme<u>ll</u> → sme<u>ll</u>s   <u>sh</u>rimp → <u>sh</u>rimps

crisp → crisps   crab → crabs

spla<u>sh</u> → spla<u>sh</u>i<u>ng</u>

Red words

my   <u>the</u>   of

5

Vocabulary check

Discuss the meaning (as used in the story) after the children have read each word.

definition:

shrimps, crabs *shellfish*

Mr Punch *a funny puppet*

Punctuation to note in this story:

Dad Mum	*Capital letters for names*
Shrimps Soft	*Capital letters that start sentences*
A Splashing	
.	*Full stop at the end of each sentence*

In the sun

Introduction

Who has been to the seaside?
What do people like to do at the seaside?
What food do they eat?

*Meg goes to the seaside with her family. She does lots of
exciting things and has lots of nice things to eat.*

Story written by Gill Munton
Illustrated by Tim Archbold

Soft wet sand,

a bucket in my hand.

Shrimps and crabs and shells,

funny fishy smells.

A ship with a flag,

yummy crisps in a bag.

Red jam in a bun,

a comic in the sun.

A can full of pop,

a net from the shop.

A stick of pink rock,

Mr Punch in his frock.

Splashing Dad and Mum,

a blob of sun stuff on my tum.

A lolly on the rug,

and milk in a mug.

I had such a lot of fun

with Mum and Dad

in the sun.

Questions to talk about

Re-read the page. Read the question to the children. Tell them whether it is a **FIND IT** question or **PROVE IT** question.

FIND IT

✓ Turn to the page

✓ Read the question

✓ Find the answer

PROVE IT

✓ Turn to the page

✓ Read the question

✓ Find your evidence

✓ Explain why

Page 8:	PROVE IT	What happens to Meg's feet in the sand? What do you think Meg is feeling? (happy, excited)
Page 9:	PROVE IT FIND IT	What does Meg catch in her net? What is on top of the ship?
Page 10:	FIND IT	What does Meg eat this time? What does she read?
Page 11:	FIND IT	What does she eat/drink/watch?
Page 12:	FIND IT	Who does she splash?
Page 13:	PROVE IT	How is Meg feeling at the end of the day?